MY FIRST STICKERS

Creepy Crawlies

Have fun completing the activities
in this creepy-crawly themed book.

*

Use your pencils to colour, doodle and
complete the activities on each page.

*

Where there is a missing sticker, you will see
an empty shape. Search your sticker pages
to find the missing sticker.

You can also press out a cute
card and beautiful bookmarks
from your card pages.

make
believe
ideas

Lovely ladybirds

Join the dots to finish the ladybird. Then, colour it in.

5   4   3

2

1

6

7

8

9

10

Find the missing stickers.

Slimy snail

Trace the trail to complete the snail.

Colour the flowers.

Find the missing stickers, and then
search the scene for the bugs listed below.
When you've found them, tick the box!

☐ 2 worms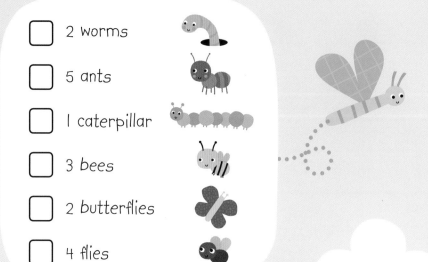

☐ 5 ants

☐ 1 caterpillar

☐ 3 bees

☐ 2 butterflies

☐ 4 flies

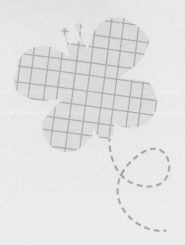

Silly spiders

Circle five differences between the scenes.

Buzzing beehive

Help Becky the bee through the beehive. Avoid the birds and the butterflies.

Start

Finish

7

Beautiful butterfly

Join the dots to complete the butterfly.

Decorate my wing.

2
•3
1•
•4
6 •
5
•7
10 •
•8
•9

Worm's words

Find the words in the grid below. Words can go down or across.

d	x	a	t	b	f
l	e	a	f	e	l
b	t	r	e	e	o
x	l	z	q	r	w
s	n	a	i	l	e
s	p	i	d	e	r

bee

flower

leaf

snail

spider

tree

Doggy doodles

Colour the picture.

Amazing answers

Find the missing stickers, and then circle the answers to the questions.

Who spins a web?

spider

snail

Who turns into a butterfly?

fly

caterpillar

Who can fly?

ant

bee

Who likes the water?

frog

butterfly

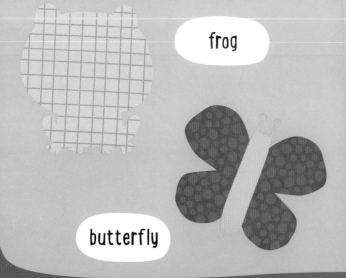

Who lives underground?

ladybird

worm

Perfect patterns

Use stickers and colour to complete the patterns.

Amazing ants

Help Andy the ant find his friends in the middle of the apple.

Start

Finish

Use the grid to help you draw the apple.

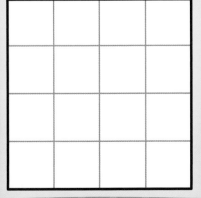

15

Pretty petals

Colour the picture using the key below.

1 2 3 4 5

Dot-to-dot card

Join the dots to finish the picture. Then press out the card, write in it, and give it to a friend.

Beautiful bookmarks

Press out the bookmarks and decorate them with your stickers.

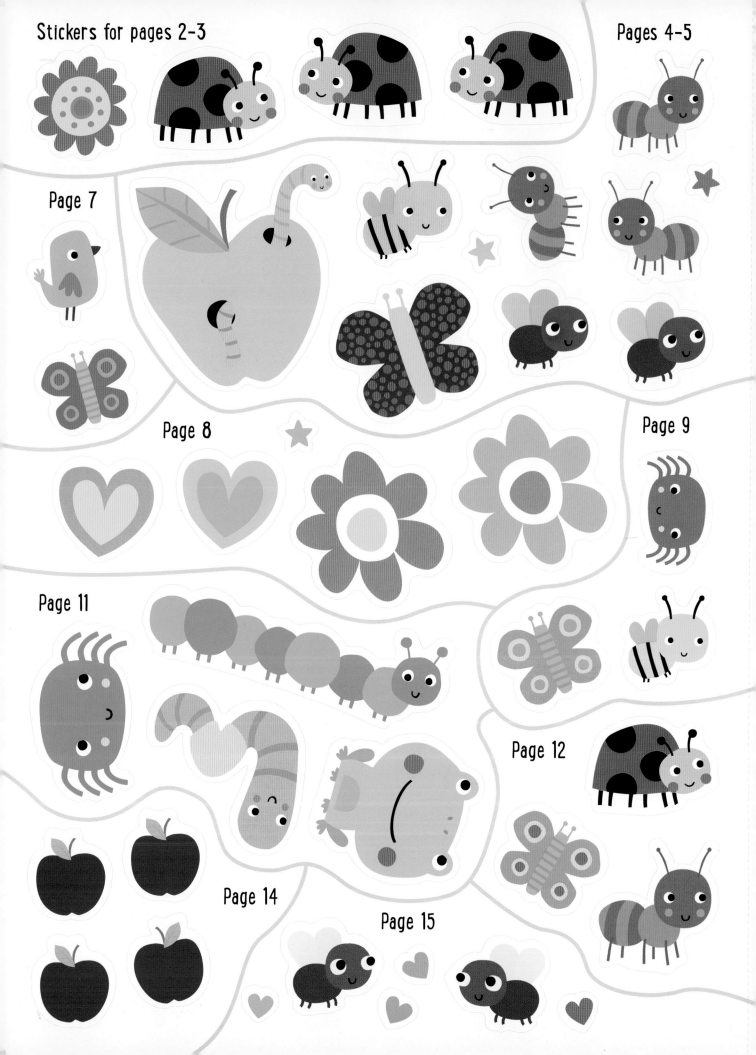

Stickers for pages 2-3

Pages 4-5

Page 7

Page 8

Page 9

Page 11

Page 12

Page 14

Page 15

Extra Stickers